The Eye *of* the Needle

Abigail Petit

Credits
Text editor Susannah Waters
Design and Layout Gaynor Warren

Publishing Information
This first edition published May 2005
Published by Gossypium
Vericott Ltd, Bellwalk House Uckfield East Sussex TN22 5DQ
Printed in Sussex by The Bridge Press
Typeset in M Perpetua, Bruce Old Style BT and Din

A catalogue for this book is available from the British Library
ISBN 0-9550391-0-X

"Work is worship"

M.K.Gandhi

Dedicated to
Aviva, Talia and Lucy
with love from Mummy.

A few weeks ago, I found myself heading unusually early in the morning down the High Street in Lewes where I live. It was a dank and drizzly grey morning, and when the card seller stepped out beside me to hang his board of cards on the front door as part of the daily ritual of opening his shop, I felt drawn in by the light and the colours in a way akin more to the exotic markets of the East than of my little English home town. However, I followed the pull, and once inside, it didn't take a second for my eye to land on a new set of cards. They each displayed a hand made toy, neatly presented in front of a pretty piece of fabric. I recognised the toys. They were made from the same pattern that I had used so long ago; the same brown wool for the Lions face, the same sloping eyes on the Rabbit - and the same 70's fabrics.

They looked so proud in the photos – and so familiar. It was only a few months since I'd written this book and my toys were still at Jenny's where she had been drawing them. "I've just written about these," I excitedly told the card seller. "They are from a new company," he replied "Why don't you give them a ring ?".

My overwhelming thought on the way home was that all the silent toys I had just written about might also have had a life.

Maybe they had changed hands, indeed when I rang the lady from the card company she talked to my amazement about "Collectors". I couldn't believe that my attraction to this sort of work was not quirky and peculiar to me, but it was happening all over. People had really kept a home made toy for 30 years and then taken his photograph and put him on a card with a smart background and sold him in a trendy card shop. The girl from the card company confirmed it "It's very of the moment," she said.

And so I deliver this book to you with more confidence than when I wrote it last year. I *have* used my personal story to tell a much bigger one. If people are appreciating home-made toys again then they are elevating them above all the rest of production. Other people *are* getting sick of all the limitless, rootless, mass-produced items.

Maybe we are all tired of pushing the bulging wardrobe door shut, or spending our Saturdays alternately shopping and stuffing the plastic bags under the sink, or sorting out the last lot of clothes to put in black bin bags on the doorstep.

Maybe we don't want to change the way we look all the time, but prefer our lived in clothes, ones that fit and that have travelled with us a while, holding memories of nice evenings;

maybe it's more fun to see our toddlers running round in things their cousins once wore.

When I quoted from William Morris in a paper I wrote as a student that "it would be merely insanity to make goods on the chance of their being wanted; for there is no longer anyone who can be compelled to buy them," I felt the idea was a bit wild and far off. But with the famous "High Street retail spending" now levelling off, I realise this vision may be about to happen in my life-time.

The movements for organic products, fair trade, and anti-sweatshop are all about valuing the producer and his or her environment. But the toy in the card shop goes further and says more.

It says what I have written about here - that being a producer is better than being a consumer. That we can simply stop consuming and spend our time differently - get good at making something instead. And that other people will then value what we have created, and we can appreciate what they have done, even if they live on the other side of the world.

I wouldn't have dared to openly make this link if not for the cards with the toys on them that found their way to Lewes last month. Its a nerve racking thing to claim that without money, marketing, professionalism, fashion, status, brands and so on, a humble, anonymous, home made toy can survive 30 years of throwaway society for a reason that's not scientific, not quantifiable, not even tangible according to the economics we base our world on.

But I know it's the reason, because it's on the back of the card. It's what I've written about in this book and other people *can* see it. I turned the card over and smiled right down to my inner eye. The name of the series was "Stuffed With Love".

Abigail Petit
Lewes,
April 2005.

O nce upon a time... *there was a little girl. She had brown hair and brown eyes and a face that made her feel she could fit in anywhere. This had its advantages people of different countries asked if she came from their country — Spain, France, Romania, Greece, Israel, Egypt, India, Bangladesh — everyone claimed her when they met her, and this made her feel very loved.*

The little girl was a happy person, full of the love of all these people, and her classmates called her "Happy Girl". Happy Girl spent a lot of time thinking about how lucky she was to have been born into a nice family, in England, where she went to a nice school and had everything she needed. She also thought a lot about people who didn't have these things and she sent big thank you's to the life force every day.

Only one side of her family was from England. The other had been uprooted and no longer lived in the country where they were born. Her grandfather's name meant "from the East" in one language while her great grandmother's name meant "castle" in another and although she had lived always in England, because of this she felt connected to far away things.

Happy Girl also had a secret — she loved to stay quietly
at home and sew.

When she was seven, her Mummy and Daddy taught her how to use a sewing machine.

Very quickly, she started cutting up the scraps of cloth that her mother gave her, stitching them front to back, turning them inside out, and stuffing the inside with chopped up bits of foam to make little toy animals and dolls. Happy Girl liked it best when it came time to make their faces, because as she stitched, the eyes, the noses, and finally the mouths came to life. It was like a new person was created with every face. Every one was different; the faces never came out the same way twice.

Happy Girl was happy making her toys and dolls. With each one, she got a little better at it. The stitching got straighter, the turning-inside out neater, the stuffing more even, the closing-up of the stuffing hole more invisible and the faces, the faces ever more life-like.

Happy Girl's friends and teachers began to ask to buy her dolls with money. At first she found this a little funny, but she was happy that people could see the life force that was inside what she had made. Gradually she found it was an even better feeling to make the toys and dolls for someone else. She realised she could think about to whom the toy was going, and she made special trims and faces to match. She liked to see the people's reactions when they received what she had made especially for them. She still found it slightly funny that they gave her money for her creations, but she didn't stop making them.

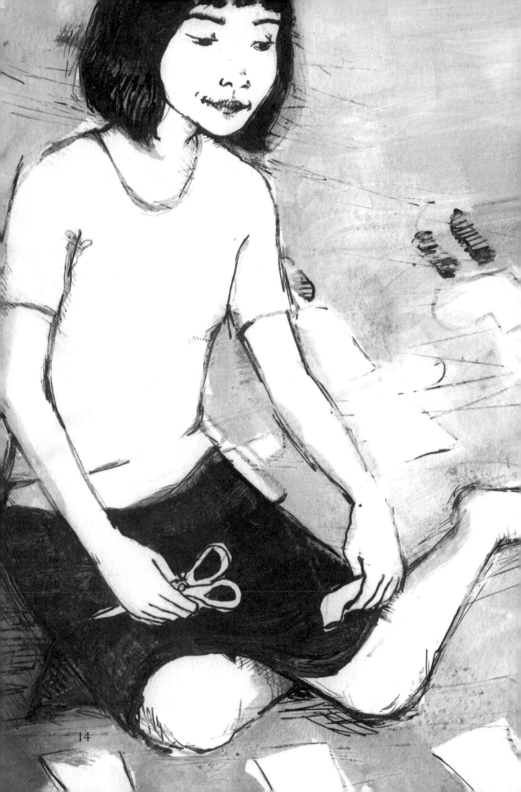

Happy Girl began to grow up. When she reached twelve years old, her friends had many worries about the way they looked and what other people thought of them.

But Happy Girl wasn't too bothered with all that. Instead of going out, she would spend her Saturday nights surrounded by a mini-production line – one evening she managed to cut out sixteen Snoopy dogs all in one sitting! If she cut out 32 arms first, she could cut a strip like this, then chop it up faster, and then the head shapes could be cut from the scraps leftover at the side. It felt like her mind and her fingers were just lying in wait to solve problems like these, each time reducing waste and valuing her resources - the tiny pieces of cloth she used. Each week, Happy Girl had 15p of pocket money to spend, and she would buy this cloth from a friendly lady who kept the smallest scraps for her under the counter.

Her fingers began to learn the feel of different fabrics. They knew as she touched them how the fabric would stretch and fold. They learned which fabrics you could fold twice before it became too thick to fit under the foot of the sewing machine. They discovered how it puckered as they fed it through, and which folding would break the needle, forcing her to cover the hole or decide it would be better to start all over again.

Her friends told Happy Girl she should be a fashion designer.

But what Happy Girl really wanted to do was help people. She had a picture of sunshine inside her mind, one of rice fields and deserts, and people working on the land.

When Happy Girl was sixteen, she suddenly had lots of new day-to-day worries. Her parents had unexpectedly split up. When you don't really come from one place, and your parents come from two different ones, and you've moved homes many times, and you're born into more than one religion, you don't really know who you are. Happy Girl lost everything. She lost her smile and she was not really Happy Girl anymore. She was scared of wasting her life – of getting in with the wrong friends, of taking drugs, or finding destructive ways out of her sadness.

But Happy Girl still had two things going for her; – her go-anywhere face linking her to all the people she met, and the fact that she could sew.

But now sewing wasn't cool. She was still known for her sewing, but the only sewing she could do without looking silly was to straighten all her friend's jeans, and patch up their holes, which was sometimes quite smelly. Once she cut up her sheets to make a skirt. She dyed the sheets yellow, so people wouldn't notice she'd used her sheets.

But no one else wore home-made clothes anymore and so, with a lot of sadness, she tucked up all she knew deep down inside her, and the thing that had connected her fingers to her eye to her heart to the smile to the force of life in people everywhere got buried. But it had left her with something special. It was like she could see the world differently through the skill of her fingers, through the Eye of her Needle.

Her work had given her an insight, an inner eye. It was as if faith, strength, a sense of self and purpose had rolled into one through her needle skills.

She didn't measure herself against anyone else. When she worked with cloth, she had felt truly herself, she had felt peaceful and friends with the world.

Now it was all gone and she was no longer happy. But she was never afraid. She had the Eye of the Needle inside her. And she still had her go-anywhere face.

So at 18 she became Searching Girl. She felt sure that other people must share her secret and Searching Girl set out to find them. She followed the signs from her inner eye, listened to no one but was open to everyone, and she always worked very hard. Her adventures lasted many years and they took her on bumpy buses, jumbo jets, and rattling taxis. Through city and village, across several continents she travelled, and she was alone most of the time. But she made many new friends on the way; some let her stay with them, others took her to new places.

Searching Girl made Five discoveries. First she learnt about looms that are used to weave threads into cloth. On these heavy metal machines fine threads are laid in one direction like hair through a comb, then a second thread is fired backwards and forwards, at right angles to the combed threads, under and over them all the way along, then back again leaving fabric behind in its path. In this way a one-dimensional long, thin piece of thread becomes a strong and flat two-dimensional structure - a piece of fabric that folds and bends but does not fall apart.

Some people Searching Girl met showed her the new looms where all you had to do was to shoot the thread across on a jet of air. The air cylinder was pressurized and you had to stand back while it was working. It took a couple of days to set up but once running it worked day and night, because it took too long to start from cold every morning. In just one day, 90 metres of cloth could be made on this loom – "more and faster" said the people who used these looms.

But Searching Girl was not excited by this "more and faster" mantra. Her Needle's Eye could only see the limitations of these machines. The weaving looked boring to make – there was nothing for a person to do – and it was boring to look at as well. No patterns, texture or lumps. And to top it all, the machines were so noisy it was like being on a building site. (You even had to wear silly ear muffs.)

"Who'd want to do that all day? " thought Searching Girl. She didn't say much though, for she wasn't sure if there was a nicer way to make cloth.

Until one day she got out of a taxi after at least six hot hours of driving from the town. She was in southern India with her friend Mr. Nanaran and she was led into a Weaver's home.

The rooms lined a courtyard where a child was idly rolling some brightly coloured threads onto a bobbin like a cotton reel. Behind him, strands of coloured yarn hung in the sun to dry. Weaving was obviously a family business, Searching Girl deduced, as she was led into the fourth and last room.

There, in pride of place was the simple wooden structure, square like the room itself. It looked a bit like those climbing frames you get in good playgrounds. A man was sitting on a bench in the middle of it, his bare feet peddling the soft wooden pedals below, his arm above pulling string with a kind of expert link to the other hand smoothing the threads. Zap and Flash. Zap and Flash. Searching Girl became Happy Girl again for a split second. She looked at the face of the man whose whole body was busy with his skill and she knew it: You could weave fabric the Needle's Eye way. She listened to the rhythmic click-clack of the wooden loom, and she saw the skill of the stripes coming out almost the same width each time. She was told that hand weavers managed about three metres per day. That's a double sheet a day, made quietly, with no electricity and no dust. No commuting for these guys either, not even a childcare problem – just a cool house design with room for a loom.

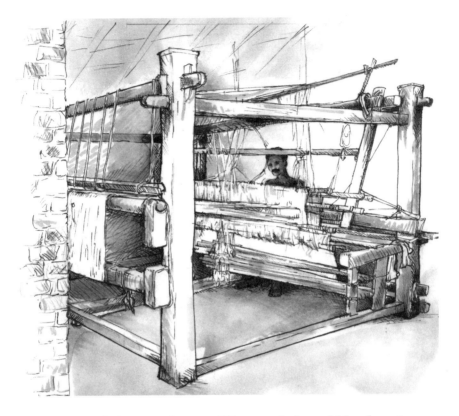

She had made her First discovery: Weaving cloth could be done in the Eye of the Needle way, if only people accepted having less of it. Searching Girl instantly committed to passing on this first secret about the "less and quieter" cloth to those who thought the "more and faster" cloth was the only option.

Next Searching Girl came on her travels to Mumbai, a big bustling city in India where she was taken into a city home. There she met a girl called Bhabhi. Although only a couple of years older than Searching Girl, she was already married to a man called Bhai, and they lived with his mother and father, sister and brother as was the custom. Bhai's mother loved embroidery and she worked with some ladies in the villages, buying it and bringing it to sell to the ladies of the city. Every piece was different and the fashionable ladies spent hours choosing the right pieces for them.

Searching Girl felt good staying at Bhabhi's house. They talked while stirring pots in the kitchen and when a customer came and Bhabhi's mother in law pulled suitcases out from under all the beds, out came the embroideries, each more beautiful than the last. Once they sold some embroidery to a diamond dealer. Searching Girl asked him if they were as beautiful as the diamonds he polished and sold for fortunes. "More beautiful," he said, for indeed they were the most amazing needlework Searching Girl had ever seen.

Searching Girl became Happy Girl as the Eye of the Needle shone out. One day they took her to the villages to meet the embroidering women. Their neat clean homes were simple and traditional, and very different from the way Searching Girl lived in England, but the way they took the cloth and their threads into their laps was exactly what Searching Girl had known.

At that moment Searching Girl realised how people are the same all over the world, and how the Eye of the Needle comes into all who work with their fingers.

She had made her Second Discovery — that embroidery is more beautiful than diamonds, that everyone can learn to do it, and that the skill of the hand leads to the Eye of the Needle inside.

Next, she saw the block printers in the nearby village. An ancient craft too, only practised by a few people in Europe. The printers carved blocks of wood with designs and used them like rubber stamps to create pictures on long pieces of cloth, laid out on the table. The printer rubbed the wooden block on a pad of ink then lifted it up, aligned his hand with his eye like a snooker player, then bang, down went the block onto the cloth. Slowly, with anticipation, he lifted it up again – Whew! He had got the position right.

Like the weaver and the embroiderer, the block printers had learned the hand-eye skill. Searching Girl liked the patterns but they looked a bit too flowery compared to the designs we get on our clothes today. They would be okay for tablecloths and curtains, she thought. The colours they used were really soft and pretty, so she asked about the inks they used. All were made locally from crushed plants and rocks. The indigo plant had to macerate in a special kind of yoghurt to ferment, she was told - it was almost like cooking.

The printers' natural ink-making had the same sense of special nurturing for which Searching Girl was looking. It was a shock when she came to compare it with a big T-shirt factory she visited next.

For the clothes we buy in the West, this kind of done-by-hand pattern printing would take too long.

The fabric that we see is usually dyed in one go, in a plain colour, in a massive washing machine which swishes the colour around as a big metal drum turns. The men who operate the machines told Searching Girl they could dye six tonnes of fabric a day – six tonnes is the weight of 120 young people – tumbling perhaps twenty at a time, all dyed in the latest colour. That's 24,000 T- shirts a day, per factory. From visiting only one of these factories, Searching Girl could only imagine just how much T-shirt fabric was being dyed per day around the world! And how many big machines were turning if we each wanted a new T-shirt every couple of weeks.

Searching Girl followed the dyeing and washing machine tubes out of the factory and down to the treatment plant where the water was cleaned up for re-use. She saw with her own eyes that it was true most of the water in the large drums did come back nice and clean, but then she also saw a thick black slime, like runny toffee, coming out of a pipe on the other side. The people at the factory told her this was the residue. Nothing more could be done with that bit – which still weighed as much as 20 young people – and it got buried in the ground, each day.

Wow, that's messy, thought Searching Girl, and she remembered the indigo plant in its natural yoghurt. We might be used to getting loads of clothes in all sorts of never-fade bright colours, but somewhere on the other side of the world the slime is creeping up on us.

She made her Third Discovery: That there is an art to natural dyeing and cloth decorating methods that are a little less permanent and take longer to do, but they are a lot less messy than the way most of our clothes are made. The price of our bright colours is hidden far away in someone elses field.

It was in Bangladesh that Searching Girl learned about sewing factories. She saw right away on her very first visit why people called them sweatshops. One kind of sweat was the sweat you produced yourself in a gym for lack of natural exercise; the other kind was the sweat brought on by the heat of the lights, the sewing machines, and the lack of windows. It was very hot inside the sweat-shirt factory, and the sewers were always sweating.

But Searching Girl, unlike everyone else, was not so upset about the bending over the machines, the bowed head and the racing, hard-working fingers.

She knew, from her own childhood hours, that it wasn't bad, to work like that. She enjoyed working with the sewing women. When she wanted to teach them how to make a new style or edge of seam, she didn't give orders or instructions from the office – she just sat behind the sewing machine and sewed.

The sewers gathered round her several layers deep. There were no words but the stitches made the language and Searching Girl became happy again for some moments as she felt at one with the sewers of the world.

So it was never the sewing that bothered Searching Girl, but she found out other things that were making these sewers sweat. Often the fabric they needed to stitch had been ordered from another country. And how much can go wrong with shipping around the world! Searching Girl learned that when the fabric got stuck at customs, the sewers had no work and had to go home and wait. But then, when it finally came, the shirts had to be sent by a certain day or the buyer's order was automatically cancelled. So the sewers had to sew faster than they ever had before, even all night, for if the order got cancelled they would have no work at all.

Searching Girl knew the owner of the sewing factory. She was a big passionate lady with thin black hair scraped back to reveal a wide, white parting. She got very upset about the fabric when it was late and the effect this had on her sewers, but there was nothing she could do about fabric getting stuck in transit, or orders automatically cancelled within the bank.

So she made her Fourth discovery:- Sewing for far-away buyers with far-away fabrics was not very practical for women who had families to look after in the evening. These sewers were not like she had been, buying her own fabric and using her skills in the community, they were locked in a big chain of events that spanned the world.

But it was Searching Girl's Fifth discovery that turned out to be the biggest of all.

One day she took a job in a factory that made fibre. Fibre is the fine stuff – no longer than half your thumb – that we use to twist into the threads and strings which we then weave or knit to form the cloth that makes our clothes. Once Searching Girl started thinking about fibre, she knew she was getting to the beginning of the story. Searching Girl knew about wool fibre from sheep and goats, and she even remembered seeing a lady knit a jumper from rabbit hair on Blue Peter when she was small.

Searching Girl also knew about cotton. She had pulled apart cotton wool balls and examined how fine and white they were. She knew that cotton grew on plants and that there were also other plants— called hemp, or jute, or linen – whose stems you could also use.

But until she took the job in the factory, Searching Girl had not fully grasped that you can also make fibres by squeezing a plastic-like liquid through a set of holes, just like making spaghetti with dough. You have to put a chemical in the liquid to make the fibre white like cotton or wool, and you have to chop it up to have the same length that cotton or wool have naturally. But other than that, it comes out fast and smooth and is really impressive to watch in the factory.

Searching Girl learned how you could make the spaghetti fibre from several different materials. There was melted-down wood, which made the shiny fabrics used in jacket linings, or plastic pellets (originally created from oil), with which you could make several different types of fibre. The one most people know best is called polyester, and it's used to make duvets, fleeces, track suits, school uniforms. Sometimes on its own, sometimes mixed with cotton. Searching Girl was interested in the spaghetti fibre. Although she didn't like the feel of it much, she didn't mind it at first. But then she realised how much of it was getting made each year. She looked on a graph and saw that it had only been invented about 60 years ago. It was used very little at the beginning, when it was new and quite expensive, and made only in America and Europe.

But now Searching Girl found out that more and more factories were being built – all over the world now, including at least 10 in China. She realised that, although when her parents were small these spaghetti fibres were hardly seen, now more and more was made each year. Far more synthetic fibres than cotton, wool, silk, linen and all the natural fibres put together. Searching Girl now understood why clothes kept getting cheaper and shops kept getting fuller – there was just so much polyester to use up!

Searching Girl looked at how the polyester was taking the place of the cotton and she began to listen out for stories from the people making cotton. The stories she heard were not surprising, and indeed they were all about how growing cotton was getting expensive because of the dependency on chemicals used as pesticide. But at the same time the price of cotton was dropping to match the price of synthetic fibres.

She had made her Fifth discovery:- Synthetic fibres were threatening the production of natural fibres and she knew this was the starting point for change. Searching Girl didn't wait any longer.

Didn't she know someone who was working in the villages, with farmers and crafts people?

And so it was that Searching Girl returned to Bhai and Bhabhi in India. Her friends gave her a place to stay and off she went, up to Kutch on the Western tip of India right on the coast.

By then Bhais mother had left the big city and lived simply in the villages near the farmers, close to the embroidering women for whom she had opened a shop nearby. When she saw that Searching Girl had come back after all these years she presented her with a big red woollen shawl. It was literally covered with embroidery done in exquisite geometric designs. This particular embroidery stitch is called Soof and is one of the ones not drawn first. The women count the threads of the fabric and the pattern just comes out of their head. It was nothing short of stunning and had taken three months to complete.

Searching Girl was overcome to receive such a present. As she put it on she not only revelled in the beauty of the item, but she knew the importance of the gift. She felt she had been handed the job of joining these remote people, with their history,culture and skills intact and linking them to the rest of the world. Searching Girl now had the shawl of responsibility on her shoulders, so she began her work.

Her friends gave her a place to stay and off she went, up to the cotton fields. She was in a little rattling car, with the windows open, she saw camels go past and people walking in the searing heat along the dusty roads. Here she found the cotton farmers.

Searching Girl was taken onto the balcony of a small, hand-built house that Bhai and the man in the car had told her belonged to a "good farmer". The words had struck her. She had learned that farmers either used chemicals for growing the plants or didn't, in which case they were "organic".

But as they walked through the small fields, she also realised that a "good farmer" was one who cared. He didn't just spray his fields with the chemical products dissolved in water and then sit down and do nothing.

He actually loved his plants, and he watched the leaves as they grew, lifting them up and looking underneath each day to check if insect life was developing. When he saw a ladybird he was happy, for he knew they would eat the bugs that ate the leaves. When he saw caterpillars, he had to act before they turned the leaf to lace by eating most of it, which weakened the plant and stopped it from growing tall and strong.

The happy farmer knew what to do about the caterpillars – he went off to fetch hand-pressed oils from other plants, such as the neem plant that also grew nearby. He knew as he squirted it on, that it would chase the caterpillars away. Searching Girl was fascinated by this skilful farmer. She sensed that he also possessed the same eye-hand-soul-skill that she called the Eye of the Needle.

Was this farmer happy in the secret way she knew? After a few more minutes of observing this man's love for his fragile plants- the waxiness of the stem and the brightness of the red flower- Searching Girl knew that he was.

Searching Girl became Happy Girl again, right on the spot, when she realised she had found what she had been looking for all this time. She could now begin with this cotton fibre, put all the steps together and make lots of products clothes, toys, whatever people wanted.

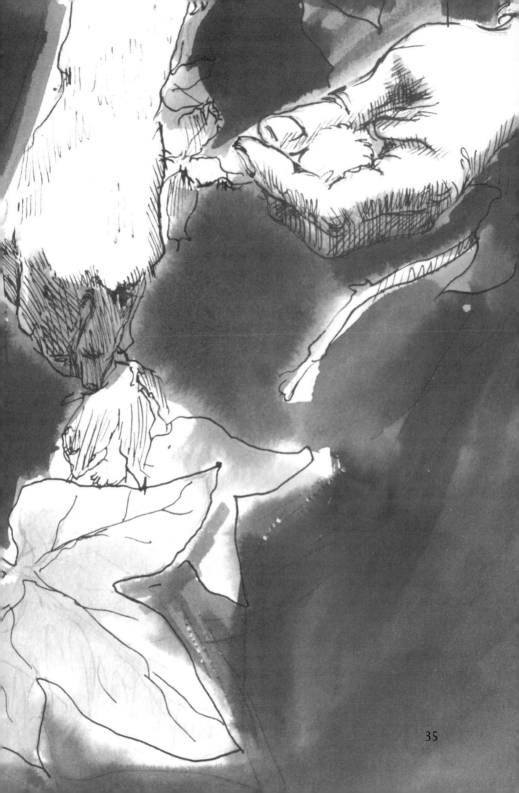

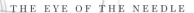

But back in Mumbai, her happiness faded as she realised how hard her dream would be to achieve. For 200 hundred years, these cotton farmers had sold their precious yearly crop for little more than the price of a refrigerator, and they didn't know life any other way. She couldn't do much to change that on her own, even with Bhai and Bhabhi's full support.

There was one thing for which Searching Girl had forgotten to search.

But the life force must have noticed because one day someone got off an aeroplane and simply started helping. He came from France and he knew a lot about textiles because his father sold beautiful, old-fashioned cloth like his father before him and his grandfather and even his great grandfather before that. The man knew about colours and prints and weaves, and about all the things Searching Girl had encountered on her travels.

His name was Tips and Bhai and Bhabhi invited him to stay.

Happy Girl and Tips, by making friends with the farmers, got to know more about cotton farming. They learned how they planted in the month of May and how it was better when they planted one row of cotton, then one row of lentils, then another row of cotton.

Happy Girl and Tips learned about how careful they had to be with water, as the cotton plant is a thirsty one. In the old days, farmers would dig channels, cleverly woven through the slopes, and the water flowed through like a marble, in those puzzles where you manoeuvre a wooden plank to get the marble to a certain place. But a lot of the water got evaporated that way; it dried up in the hot Indian sun. So the farmers, working with Bhai and his farming co-ordinator Hasmi, used a thing called drip irrigation, where a thin black hose pipe lies between the plants and lets out drips around the root of each plant.

Hasmi explained that they could keep a field healthy with no more than 5 bathfuls of water per field this way. Not 40, as was the case with the old way. Using water carefully was an important part of Hasmi's cotton growing skill.

Like everyone around him, Hasmi valued natural resources, and working with nature was at the heart of what he did. Although Tips and Happy Girl brought studies from England describing organic farming standards, Hasmi's farmers got busy in their own way.

One day Tips and Happy Girl walked through the fields and saw a series of poles in the middle of the field – like half-built tree houses. The farmers told them they'd spotted that the cotton around the edge of the fields was the best. And they realised that birds were sitting on the hedges at the edge of the fields, then swooping in and eating the insects sitting on nearby cotton plants. So the tree houses they'd placed across the fields were bird perches, in the hope that more birds would come and eat insects from all the plants!

There was no doubt that the first crop of much loved Eye of the Needle grown cotton was healthy. The plants were strong with waxy stems, as only healthy plants have, with about 10 balls of cotton on each plant. They had taken eight months to grow, from planting through to the red flowering stage, to the time when the buds popped open to show the fluffy cotton fibre inside.

The cotton was now ready for picking. It was looking beautiful. When Tips and Happy Girl looked at cotton grown in the normal way, they saw that rushed picking meant that brown bits of husk were collected along with the soft, pure cotton balls. They also saw, when they were all tipped into a pile, that strands of the jute bags that were used to collect the cotton - got mixed in as well. They knew this led to brown bits in the fabric later – which would have to be bleached out again with strong chemicals.

So Tips and Hasmi worked with the farmers all the way through. On the day we saw the first cotton spun onto a reel at the cotton mill, the man behind the desk (who had laughed at us the first time we came with our farmers' cotton) smiled widely and put two bobbins of freshly-spun cotton on the table. "Which one is yours?" he joked.

What a great material they had now, to turn into clothes

We all smiled together because we could see the cotton our farmers had personally picked: it was pure white, clean and shiny. The secret we all shared deep inside became apparent. Truly beautiful products are the result of human skill and nurturing care, naturally in tune with nature.

Tips and Happy Girl stayed in India with the farmers for almost two years. They tried to build a sun-drier so that they could make their clothes themselves, but it didn't work. They were going to have to deal with the factories to turn their cotton into the kind of clothes that people expected – at least in the beginning.

So they made T-shirts in the nicest factory they could find and soon realised they had to come back to England to sell them. With each farmer spending eight months to grow his cotton – planting, nurturing and fertilising the red flowers and then picking eight to ten heads per plant – Tips and Happy Girl figured it would take three plants worth of cotton to make just one T-shirt. But also they counted that one could fit about 3000 plants in a farmer's typical field. So in order to buy one farmer's cotton they needed to sell one thousand T-shirts. They also knew that there were about two million cotton farmers still working in India, each with a family, meaning if they could support this kind of farming, lots more children could grow up in the countryside, with clean air and space to run around in.

Tips and Happy Girl knew they had to work fast and well, because they knew some farmers were starting to give up. Drinking their pesticides out of despair as the cost of the chemicals got higher, some farmers were actually dying. The prices they received from the traders were lower than ever before. And the farmers could not argue with these traders. The farmers did not know that there was another fibre used to make clothing. A fibre made in a factory, from oil, so abundant, cheap and fast to make that it was everywhere. More and more of it was being dyed in big machines and stitched in far away factories.

Tips and Happy Girl thought about the big factories making the fibres, and all the other big factories their fine soft cotton would have to pass through. They thought of how massive the shops were that sold clothes in the High Street. By contrast, they were so tiny and fragile, these independent farmers with their fields no bigger than some people's gardens, relying only on their fingers and ability to work with nature. But Tips and Happy Girl were not afraid.

They trusted each other and their new friends. They felt small in their huge task, but they didn't mind. They had the secret of how to make fine cloth.

A secret that had almost been lost.

Tips and Happy Girl came to England with their clothes. They talked to all the big shops, but everything went very slowly. It seemed each person they talked to was not free to change his ways like the farmers were. He or she was almost always part of a very large company instead. Tips and Happy Girl began to get worried. If they didn't sell their T-shirts, they would have to get another job to live.

They had to find people who were free to change their ways.

It was the end of May and a peace festival had come to Brighton near where they lived. They quickly printed Tip's designs on the T-shirts, and some postcards with messages like "Express yourself", and they stood behind their stall on the beach. They met ten people that day who wanted to change and were free to buy their T-shirts. Tips and Happy Girl were very happy because they knew that, while they had left Hasmi with his farmers in India, they would now work at home for a group of people who wanted to buy their clothes. It was time to create a community of customers to serve Hasmi's community of farmers. Happy Girl thought of how it had felt, so long ago, when she made people truly happy with what she made for them. Now she was grown up and doing it properly. Only this time, she knew everything about it, right back to the fibre growing on a plant in a field.

Tips and Happy Girl soon opened a shop and a website and a mail order catalogue. Now they talk to all their customers and to people who are free to change their ways and buy their clothes. Through Tips and Happy Girl, people can understand how peacefully these clothes have been made, how gently, and with what skill and care.

Happy Girl and Tips love their work and all the friends they have made.

They worked without stopping for several years and one day they realised that each of them had, in a way, done it for the other. They realised that when times were hard they had kept going so as not to let the other one down. They were true partners and their friendship had created a balance. They realised that they loved each other and one day decided to get married.

So now Tips runs the business they have created, making the clothes for the people who can understand about the fine gentle cotton and who choose to buy it. And Happy Girl has decided she must go out and tell her story.

The story of her searching and the Five discoveries she made, the story of how she used the insight from her deeply-learned skill in her fingers, to lead her back to happiness.

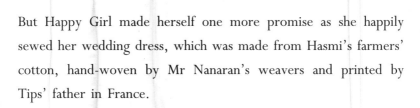

But Happy Girl made herself one more promise as she happily sewed her wedding dress, which was made from Hasmi's farmers' cotton, hand-woven by Mr Nanaran's weavers and printed by Tips' father in France.

Her promise was that she would go back to making her own clothes again, and encourage others to pick up their needles and sew.

And one day, if Happy Girl does her work well and lots of people begin sewing, then Tips will be able to sell fabrics again, like his father and his grandfather and his great grandfather did before him.

ACKNOWLEDGEMENTS

Before the people who helped me write this book, come those who made the story – beginning with my mother and father, Alegra and Paul Garner, my sister Ruth who brought me lots of childhood orders, my brother Joe, and my Omi – Irma Cullum.

Then Dipesh and Preeti Shroff, and Hasmukh Patel of Agrocel, our friends and business partners first in trust, now on paper; and my husband Thomas.

I would also like to thank some of the friends and teachers who have steered, supported or inspired me and later us; people who in so doing have put something of themselves into this story and made it real.

Laurent Lipmanowicz, Sarah Davies, Gaby Waters, Andy Fingret, Mick Hodgkin, Delia and Sian Davin, Richard Evans, Sally Ann Hooper, Joya Poti, Mr Nagarajan, Michael Hann, Kirit Dave, the whole family Shroff, Michel Grawez, Camille Blum, Gilly Weinstein, Anne and Finn Kennedy, Rebecca Vanhatalo and my friends at Lewes Quaker meeting.

Now coming to the book itself, Intrepid Theatre Company whose Arts and Business project with Gossypium gave rise to the need for this story to be written down.

Jenny Davies, Susannah Waters and Gaynor Warren who also each live a short walk from our home and who have added so much to the text with their insightful drawing, writing and graphic design skills respectively.

To the girls of 1ST Plumpton Girl Guides who urged me to get it published.

To our staff, and finally to all the customers of Gossypium, the early ones who allowed us to be born as a company, and the present and future ones whose custom makes everything possible.

February 28th 2005

We have in front of us a vision - a viable and a workable vision connecting the people together across the world.

Now, when the world is not going to have cheap oil anymore, the opportunity of togetherness is emerging.

What is emerging, is a new spirit of togetherness, serving the producers and the consumers across the world.

Not working for one's greed, but working to create a world of love and service.

This is no more an idle dream. But, with a missionary zeal, this work is progressing.

This is the new world that, together we will build, creating a life that God wants us to live.

K.C. SHROFF   **CHANDA K. SHROFF**

Kantisen Shroff as mentioned in **Prophets of New India:** Twenty social workers who transformed the lives of thousands of people.
Penguin Books India April 2004.

Chandaben Shroff founded Shrujan over 30 years ago which now works with 16 different styles of embroidery, done by 3,500 women across 100 villages, providing a unique and sustainable means of income.

THE EYE OF THE NEEDLE